mini bumper
book of

SONGS

Production:
Sadie Cook and Miranda Steel
Cover design: Glide Design

Published 1999

**International
MUSIC
Publications**

International Music Publications Limited
Griffin House 161 Hammersmith Road London W6 8BS England

The Ash Grove (Llwyn On)

Welsh Traditional

4

ash grove a - lone is my home.
wyr gam I fyn wes ei ferch.

2. Rhy hwyr ydoedd galw y saeth at llinyn
A'r llances yn marw yn welw a gwan;
Bygythiodd ei gleddyf trwy galon y llencyn
Ond ni redai cariad un fod fedd o'r fan
R'oedd golud ei darpar yn hen ac anynad
A geiriau diweddaf yr aeres hardd hon.
Oedd gwell gennyf farw drwy ergyd fy nghariad
Na byw gyda golad ym mhalas Llwyn on.

2. My lips smile no more, my heart lose its lightness
No dreams of the future my spirit can cheer,
I only would brood on the part and it's brightness
The dead I have mourn'd are again living here.
From ev'ry dark nook they press forward to meet me
I lift up my eyes to the broad leafy dome,
And others are there looking downwards to greet me,
The ash grove, the ash grove alone is my home.

Beautiful Garden Of Roses

Words by J E Dempsey
Music by Johann C Schmid

one who is fair - er than all!
charm that can nev - er de - cay.

A♭°   D♭7   C

Beau - ti - ful gar - den of ro - ses,

F   F°

Kiss'd by the gold - en dew,

C7   F

Each pret - ty flow - er dis - clos - es,

F   A

Because

French Words and Music by Guy d'Hardelot
English Words by Edward Teschemacher

Believe Me If All Those Endearing Young Charms

Words and Music by Thomas Moore

Lyrics:
1. Be - lieve me if all those en - dear - ing young charms, Which I gaze on so fond - ly to - day, Were to change by to - mor - row and flee in my arms, Like

2. It is not while beau - ty and youth are thine own, And thy cheeks un - pro - faned by a tear, That the fer - vour and faith of a soul can be known, To which

Bird Songs At Eventide

Words by Royden Barrie
Music by Eric Coates

Bless This House

Words by Helen Taylor
Music by May H Brahe

Cobbler's Song

Words by Oscar Asche
Music by Frederic Norton

David Of The White Rock
(Dafydd Y Gareg Wen)

Welsh Traditional

2. Neithiwr mi glywais lais angel fel hyn:
"Dafydd, tyr'd adref a chwar trwy'r glyn"
Delynfy mebyd! ffarwel i dy dant
Duw a'ch bendithio, fyngweddw a'm plant.

2. Give me my harp, my companion so long,
Let it once more add it's voice to my song,
Though my old fingers are palsied and weak
Still my good harp for it's master will speak.

The Diver

Words by G Douglas Thompson
Music by E H Loder

fear - ful such sights ___ to the di - ver must be, Walk - ing a - lone,

Eb   Eb7   Ab   F7   Bb

cresc.   _pp_   _unis._

walk - ing a - lone, walk - ing a - lone in the depths of the sea!

Eb   Abo   Eb   Bb7   Eb

_mf_

Eb   Bb7   Eb   F7   Eb   Bb7   Eb

_mf_

He is now on the sur - face (he's gasp - ing for breath,') So

Cm   Ab   G

Drink To Me Only With Thine Eyes

Words by Ben Johnson
Music Traditional

Brown Bird Singing

Words by Royden Barrie
Music by Haydn Wood

The English Rose

Words by Basil Hood
Music by Edward German

For You Alone

Words by P J O'Reilly
Music by Henry E Geehl

Gendarmes Duet

Words by H B Farnie
Music by Offenbach

In march time

And ot ou -selves we take good
Then lit -tle but -ter -flies we
And punch each oth -er's heads at

1. We're pub -lic guard -ians, bold, yet war -y,
2. Some-times our du -ty's ex -tra -mu -ral,
3. If gen -tle -men will make a ri -ot,

care!
chase,
night,

When dan -ger
Com-mune with
Pro -vi -ded

To risk our pre -cious lives we're char -y,
We like to gam -bol in things ru -ral,
We're quite dis -pos'd to keep it qui -et,

looms, we're ne - ver there!
na - ture face to face!
that they make it right!

But when we meet a help - less
Un - to our beat then back re -
But if they do not seem to

Or lit - tle boys that do no harm,
Re-freshed by na - ture's ho - ly charm,
Or give to us our pro - per terms!

wo - man,
turn - ing,
see it,

We run them
We run them
We run them

We run them in,
We run them in,
We run them in,

we run them in,
we run them in,
we run them in,

We show them
We show them
We show them

in,
in,
in,

we run them in,
we run them in,
we run them in,

cresc.

I'll Sing Thee Songs Of Araby

Words by W G Wills
Music by Frederick Clay

The Gentle Maiden

Words and Music by J J Pain

Gipsy's Warning

Words and Music by Henry A Goard

1. Do not trust him gen - tle la - dy, Tho' his voice be low and
2. Do not . turn so cold - ly from me, I would on - ly guard thy
3. La - dy once there lived a maid - en, Pure and bright and like thee
4. Keep thy gold I do not wish it! La - dy I have prayed for

sweet, Heed not him who kneels be - fore you, Gent - ly
youth From his stern and with' - ring pow - er, I would
fair, But he wooed, and wooed, and won her, Fill'd her
this, For the hour when I might foil him, Rob him

plead - ing at thy feet, Now thy life is in __ its
on - ly tell thee truth, I would shield thee from _ all
gen - tle heart with care, Then he heed - ed not __ her
of ex - pect - ed bliss, Gen - tle la - dy, do __ not

Goodnight

Words by Adrian Ross
Music by Eduard Kunneke

I Know Of Two Bright Eyes (Myrra)

Words and Music by G H Clutsum

I'll Walk Beside You

Words by Edward Lockton
Music by Alan Murray

55

In An Old-Fashioned Town

Words by Ada Leonora Harris
Music by W H Squire

Jeanie With The Light Brown Hair

Words and Music by Stephen C Foster

Joggin' Along The Highway

Words and Music by Arthur Anderson and Harold Samuel

Kashmiri Song (Pale Hands I Love You)

Words by Lawrence Hope
Music by Amy Woodforde Finden

Moderato assai, con molto sentimento

1. Pale hands I loved beside the Shali-mar,*
2. Pale hands, pink tipped, like Lo-tus bud that float

Where are you now? Who lies be-neath your spell? Whom do you lead on
On those cool wa-ters where we used to dwell. I would have ra-ther

Rap-ture's road-way, far, Be-fore you a-go-nise them in fare-well?
felt you round my throat Crush-ing out life, than wav-ing me fare-well!

Keys Of Heaven

Words and Music by Lucy Broadwood and Maitland Fuller
Arranged by Ernest Newton

In The Gloaming

Words by Meta Orred
Music by Annie Fortescue Harrison

72

Leanin'

Words by Hugh E Wright
Music by T Sterndale Bennett

Loch Lomond

Traditional

The Lost Chord

Words by Adelaide A Procter
Music by Sir Arthur Sullivan

Love's Garden Of Roses

Words by Ruth Rutherford
Music by Haydn Wood

Love's Old Sweet Song

Words and Music by J L Molloy and G Clifton Bingham

1. Once in the dear dead days be-yond re-call, When on the world the
2. E-ven to-day we hear loves song of yore, Deep in our hearts it

Love Sends A Little Gift Of Roses

Words by Leslie Leonard Cooke
Music by John Openshaw

1. Take thou my gift, my of - fer - ing of ros - es,
2. Take thou my gift, and be it joy or sor - row,

Cull'd from my gar - den, sweet with twi - light dew;
Think ere my ro - ses fade and fall a - part,

If just one flow'r up - on your breast re - po - ses
With each sweet bloom that you may scorn to - mor - row

Miner's Dream

Words and Music by Will Goodwin and Leo Dryden

My Ain Folk

Words by Winifred Mills
Music by Laura G Lemon

Oft In The Stilly Night

Words by Thomas Moore
Music Traditional arranged by Arther Somervell

smiles, the tears of child - hood's years, The words of love then spo - ken, The
feel like one who treads a - lone some ban - quet hall de - sert - ed, Whose
Ab Eb7 Fm C7 Fm Eb7 Ab
eyes that shone, now dimm'd and gone, The cheer - ful heart now bro - ken.
lights are fled, whose gar - lands dead, And all but me de - part - ed.
Ab Cm Db Eb7 Ab Eb7 Ab
Thus in the stil - ly night ere slum - ber's chain has bound me;
Thus in the stil - ly night ere slum - ber's chain has bound me;
C Fm Eb Ab Eb7 Ab
D.C.
Fond mem - 'ry brings the light of oth - er days a - round me.
Sad mem - 'ry brings the light of oth - er days a - round me.
Fine
Ab7 Db Ab Eb7 Ab

On The Road To Mandalay

Words by Rudyard Kipling
Music by Oley Speaks

Passing By

Words by Herrick
Music by Edward C Purcell

1. There is a la - dy sweet and kind,
2. ges - tures, mo - tions, and her smile, Her
3. Cu - pid is wing - ed and doth range Her

Was nev - er face so pleas'd my mind;
wit, Her voice my heart be - guile, Be -
coun - try, So my love doth change

I did but see her pass - ing by, And
guile my heart I know not why, And

A Perfect Day

Words and Music by Carrie Jacobs-Bond

1. When you come to the end of a per - fect day, And you
2. (Well) this is the end of a per - fect day, Near the

sit a - lone with your thought, ____ While the chimes ring out with a
end of a jour - ney ____ too; ____ But it leaves a thought that is

car - ol gay For the joy that the day has brought, ____ Do you
big and strong, With a wish that is kind and true. ____ For

Rocked In The Cradle Of The Deep

Words by Emma Hart Willard
Music by Joseph P Knight

Off To Philadelphia

Words revised and edited by Stephen Temple
Adapted from an old Irish melody by Battison Haynes

fore the break of morn,____ Faith! 'tis they'll be all for - lorn,____ For I'm
heart is sad and wear - y, How can she be Miss - es Lear - y, If I
tears will sure - ly blind me, For the friends I lave be - hind me, When I

D   E   D   A7   D   E7/A   A   A7

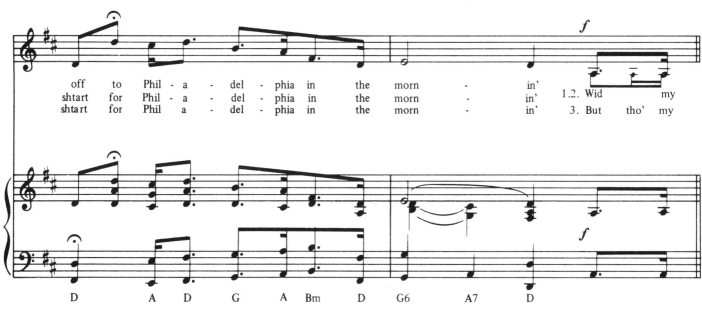

off to Phil - a - del - phia in the morn - in' 1.2. Wid my
shtart for Phil a - del - phia in the morn - in' 3. But tho' my
shtart for Phil a - del - phia in the morn - in'

D   A   D   G   A   Bm   D   G6   A7   D

CHORUS

bun - dle on my shoul - der Faith! there's no man could be boul - der, I'm
bun - dle's on my shoul - der, And there's no man could be boul - der, Tho' I'm

D

The Rose Of Tralee

Words by C Mordaunt Spencer
Music by Charles W Glover

Roses Of Picardy

Words by Fred E Weatherley
Music by Haydn Wood

Sanctuary

Words by Edward Lockton
Music by Thomas Hewitt

She Is Far From The Land

Words by Tom Moore
Music by Frank Lambert

Simon The Cellarer

Words by W H Bellamy
Music by J L Hatton

Sylvia

Words by Clinton Schollard
Music by Oley Speaks

Somewhere A Voice Is Calling

Words by Eileen Newton
Music by Arthur F Tate

The Sunshine Of Your Smile

Words by Leonard Cooke
Music by Lilian Ray

1. Dear face that holds so sweet a smile for me, Were you not mine, how
2. Sha - dows may fall up - on the land and sea, Sun - shine from all the

dark the world would be! I know no light a -
world may hid - den be; But I shall see no

bove that could re - place Love's ra - diant sun - shine in your dear, dear face.
cloud a - cross the sun; Your smile shall light my life, till life is done!

Sussex By The Sea

Words and Music by W Ward-Higgs

Marcia

1. Now is the time for
2. Up in the morn - ing
3. Some - times your feet are
4. Light is the love of a
5. Far o'er the seas we

march - ing, Now let your hearts be gay,
ear - ly, Start at the break of day;
wea - ry, Some - times the way is long,
sol - dier, That's what the la - dies say;
wan - der, Wide thro' the world we roam;

Hark to the mer - ry bu - gles Sound - ing a - long our
March till the eve - ning sha - dows Tell us it's time to
Some - times the day is drea - ry, Some - times the world goes
Light - ly he goes a woo - ing, Light - ly he rides a -
Far from the kind hearts yon - der, Far from our dear old

way. So let your voi - ces ring, my boys, And
stay. We're al - ways mov - ing on, my boys, So
wrong; But if you let your voi - ces ring, Your
way. In love and war we al - ways are As
home; But ne'er shall we for - get, my boys, And
G
C G7 C
take the time from me, And I'll sing you a song as we
take the time from me, And ___ sing this song as we
care will fly a - way, So we'll sing a song as we
fair as fair can be, And a sol - dier boy is the
true we'll ev - er be To the girls so kind that we
F G7 C11 G7 C G7
march a - long, Of Sus - sex - by - the - Sea! For
march a - long, Of Sus - sex - by - the - Sea. For
march a - long, Of Sus - sex - by - the - Sea. For
la - dies joy In Sus - sex - by - the - Sea. For
left be - hind In Sus - sex - by - the - Sea. For
C F C C G7 C

Tom Bowling

Words and Music by Charles Dibden

Trees

Words by Joyce Kilmer
Music by Oscar Rasbach

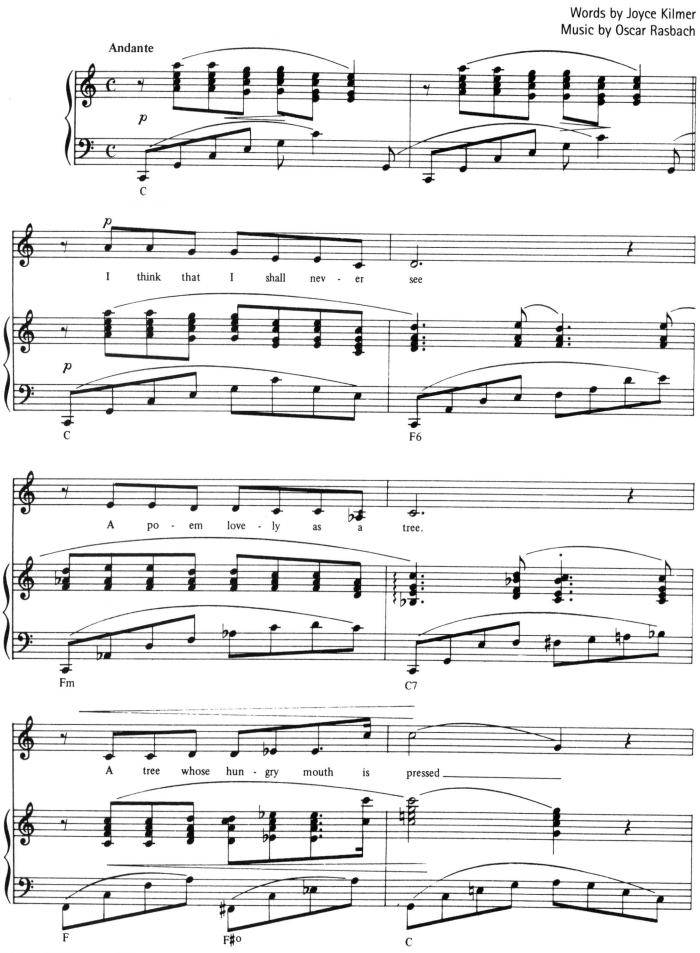

Warner/Chappell Music Ltd, London W6 8BS and International Music Publications Limited, London W6 8BS

There's A Long, Long Trail A-Winding

Words by Stoddard King
Music by Zo Elliott

148

Twickenham Ferry

Words and Music by Theo Marzials

1. O - hoi - ye - ho, Ho - ye - ho, who's for the fer - ry, (the
2. O - hoi - ye - ho, Ho - ye - ho, I'm for the fer - ry, (the
3. O - hoi - ye - ho ho! You re too late for the fer - ry, (the

bri - ar's in bud, the___ sun go - ing down,) and I'll row ye so quick and I'll
bri - ar's in bud, the___ sun go - ing down,) and it's late as it is and I
bri - ar's in bud, the___ sun go - ing down,) and he's not row - ing quick and he's

row ye so stead - y, and 'tis but a pen - ny to Twick - en - ham Town, The
have - n't a pen - ny, and how shall I get me to Twick - en - ham Town; She'd a
not row - ing stead - y, you'd think t'was a jour - ney to Twick - en - ham Town. "O

When You And I Were Young, Maggie

Words by George W Johnson
Music by J A Butterfield

When You Come Home

Words by Fred E Weatherley
Music by W H Squire

Where My Caravan Has Rested

Words by Edward Teschemacher
Music by Hermann Löhr

159

The Wolf

Words and Music by Shield

At the peace-ful mid-night hour, Ev'-ry sense and ev'-ry power

Fet-ter'd lies— in down-y sleep, Then— our care-ful watch— we keep,

Then— our care-ful watch— we keep. While the wolf in night-ly prowl,

Woodman, Spare That Tree

Words by P Morise
Music by Henry Russell

Andante con anima ed espress

1. Wood - man, spare that tree!_____ Who's
2. Old fam - il - iar tree._____ Are

Touch not a sin - gle ___ bough; In
glo - ry and ___ re - nown. Are

Printed and bound in Great Britain by Caligraving Limited 3/99